Peter Lancett is a writer, editor and film maker. He has written many books, and has just made a feature film, *The Xlitherman*.

Peter now lives in New Zealand and California.

Dark Man

The Dark Scroll

by Peter Lancett

illustrated by Jan Pedroietta

Published by Ransom Publishing Ltd.

Radley House, 8 St. Cross Road, Winchester, Hampshire
SO23 9HX

www.ransom.co.uk

ISBN   978 184167 988 4

First published in 2010

Copyright © 2010 Ransom Publishing Ltd.

Text copyright © 2010 Peter Lancett
Illustrations copyright © 2005, 2006 Jan Pedroietta

Dark Man

The Dark Scroll

by Peter Lancett

illustrated by Jan Pedroietta

Ransøm

The Dark Scroll
The Players

 The Dark Man
(114 words)

 Narrator
(93 words)

 Amanda
(74 words)

 The Old Man
(50 words)

 Demon
(28 words)

 Young boy
(25 words)

 Sister
(22 words)

 Shadow Master
(13 words)

The Dark Scroll
The Acts

Act One:
Amanda

Narrator:
The Old Man has called the Dark Man to him.

The Old Man:
This is Amanda. She has helped us in the past. She is very sick.

The Dark Man:
Did the Shadow Masters
do this? Is it their evil
magic?

Amanda:
   They sent a demon into my
   dreams to poison me.

The Old Man:
> A magic scroll was hidden years ago. If you bring it to me, I can save Amanda.

The Dark Man:
> Where is this magic scroll?

Amanda:
> That is a secret, guarded by a water demon. I can take you to the demon.

Act Two:
At the Sea Shore

Narrator:
Amanda has led the Dark Man to the sea shore.

The Dark Man:
You look tired. Let's stop and eat.

Amanda:
No. We need to find the demon before dark.

The Dark Man:
> How do I make the demon tell us where the scroll is?

Amanda:
> If you kill it, I will know what it knows. But you will be in danger.

Narrator:
Amanda starts to cry.

The Dark Man:
Don't worry. I have fought
demons before.

Amanda:
Why are you risking your
life for me?

The Dark Man:
> You are brave and you are good. And you remind me of someone.

Amanda:
> A girl you loved. I can tell.

Act Three:
The Demon

Narrator:
Amanda and the Dark Man have found the cave where the demon lives.

Demon:
You have come for the secret of the scroll. But you must fight me to get it.

The Dark Man:
> You do not frighten me. I
> have power of my own.

Demon:
> Your lack of fear ... it is
> killing me! I am dying!

Narrator:
The demon explodes.

Amanda:
It's working! I know where the scroll is!

Narrator:
The Dark Man has brought Amanda back to the city.

The Old Man:
You did well. But there is no time to rest.

The Dark Man:
I know. Amanda is next door. She is very sick.

The Old Man:
Get the magic scroll. Then bring Amanda to me.

Act Four:
The Scroll

Narrator:
> The Dark Man has met a
> young boy in the forest.

The Dark Man:
> So, you can take me to
> the magic scroll.

Young boy:
> Yes, I can. The scroll is with
> my sister.

Narrator:

The boy seems to reach inside his sister.

Sister:

We have been waiting for so long. Take the scroll. Set us free.

Young boy:
> Here, take it. Set us free.

The Dark Man:
> What do you mean, set you free?

Sister:
You have the scroll now.

Young boy:
So now we can return to
the Realm of Stars.

Sister:
Use the scroll wisely.

Narrator:
> The Dark Man is carrying Amanda to the Old Man.

The Dark Man:
> I must put you down. There are demons up ahead.

Narrator:
> The Dark Man fights off the demons. A Shadow Master screams from a rooftop.

Shadow Master:
> We will come for you one day, Dark Man. We will kill you!

The Dark Man:
> They will never beat us, Amanda. I will never let them. Never.

More **Dark Man** books:

Stories

Plays